LIST OF FLOWERS

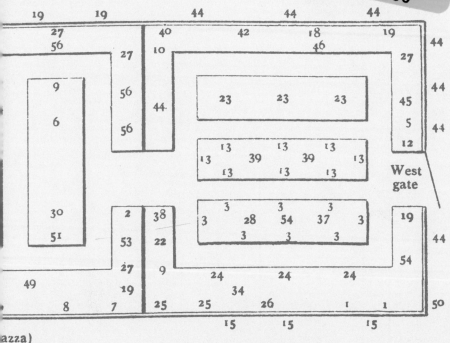

(azza)

29 Lilies	44 Sweet Peas
30 Love-in-a-Mist	45 Sweet Rocket
31 Margaret Pinks	46 Sweet William
32 Marigolds	47 Sunflowers
33 Mignonette	48 Tall Phlox
34 Oriental Poppy	49 Tea Roses
35 Peonies	50 Travelers' Joy
36 Picotee Pinks	51 Verbenas
37 Poppies	52 Vines
38 Rose-colored Iceland Poppies	53 Violets
39 Rose Campion	54 Wallflowers
40 Scotch Roses	55 Water Lilies
41 Shirley Poppies	56 White Lilies
42 Single Dahlias	57 Wistaria
43 Snowdrops, etc.	

nded by a border of all sorts of mixed flowers. A bank of flowers

AN ISLAND GARDEN DAYBOOK
BY CELIA THAXTER

WITH PAINTINGS BY
CHILDE HASSAM

AN ISLAND GARDEN
DAYBOOK

BY CELIA THAXTER
WITH PICTURES AND
ILLUMINATIONS BY
CHILDE HASSAM

HOUGHTON MIFFLIN COMPANY
BOSTON

Editor's Note

A HUNDRED YEARS AGO, Celia Thaxter, a well-known New England poet and short story writer, created the garden of this book on a rocky, windswept island ten miles off the coast of New Hampshire. It was a small, old-fashioned flower garden, but one of the most admired and painted in America. In particular, it was an inspiration to Childe Hassam, whose *Island Garden* paintings have been called as important to American Impressionism as Monet's paintings of his garden at Giverny are to French Impressionism.

Celia Thaxter was the daughter of a lighthouse keeper who brought his family to a tiny, treeless, rocky outpost, one of the Isles of Shoals, when she was four years old. At high tide the island was no bigger than an acre. For eight years Celia lived here, with only her family and a herd of goats for company. And it was here that she became a gardener. As she recalls in *An Island Garden*, "A lonely child, living on the lighthouse island ten miles away from the mainland, every blade of grass that sprang out of the ground, every humblest weed, was precious in my sight, and I began

a little garden when not more than five years old."

In 1848 Celia's father bought Hog Island, the largest of the Isles of Shoals, and moved his family there. He renamed the island Appledore and built a resort hotel, one of the first in the country, which became a vacation retreat for such literary New Englanders as Henry David Thoreau, James Russell Lowell, John Greenleaf Whittier, Sarah Orne Jewett, and Nathaniel Hawthorne, who called the young Celia "the pretty little Miranda" of the islands. (In later life, she was a member of this literary circle.)

Celia lived on Appledore Island until she was sixteen, when she married her tutor and moved with him to Newtonville, Massachusetts, near Boston. The couple had three boys, one of them mentally disturbed, and life was not easy for Mrs. Thaxter. Her husband never "found" himself professionally, and the family lived on such minimal support as his father offered. Nor was Levi Thaxter supportive of his wife's writing, although her poetry, for which she was best known during her lifetime, was published in *The Atlantic*, *Harper's*, and other magazines.

Celia Thaxter took painting lessons from a young man with the French-sounding name of Childe Hassam; supposedly it was she who convinced him to Americanize the pronunciation to Child Has´-sam. And every summer she returned to her beloved island. Her husband refused to go back after nearly drowning in a storm in 1855, and increasingly the couple led separate lives.

After her parents died, Thaxter moved into their cottage and devoted herself to gardening. Although she spoke of it modestly, her garden was spectacular. In a fenced area fifteen by fifty feet, she grew fifty varieties of flowers, most of them considered old-fashioned even in her day—hollyhocks, sunflowers, cornflowers, sweet peas, lupines, wallflowers, larkspurs, peonies, old roses, and above all, her greatest love, poppies.

In *An Island Garden,* which she wrote in response to the many visitors who asked, "How do you make your plants flourish like this?" Thaxter describes how each winter in her Portsmouth home she sowed thousands of seeds, many of them in eggshells so they could be planted intact, without disturbing the delicate roots; how she ferried her seedlings across often stormy March seas to the island; and how she tended her garden, starting work at 4 A.M. (No longer were even the humblest weeds precious in her sight.) And every day she arranged fresh flowers in a hundred vases in her cottage, where she presided over a literary, artistic, and musical salon. Childe Hassam was a frequent visitor, and the twelve paintings he did for the book were one of his earliest commissions.

Celia Thaxter died on Appledore just five

months after her book was published, in 1894. At her funeral, Childe Hassam gathered bayberry branches to lay on her grave.

And her garden?

"The sad thing about gardens," wrote Allen Lacy in an introduction to the new edition of *An Island Garden,*

> is that they often do not survive their gardeners, or they don't survive them very long. And thus it was with Celia Thaxter's island garden. Relatives kept it up for a while, and visitors came regularly in the summer to see her parlor, with its grand piano, its wall covered with paintings by Childe Hassam and other friends, and its many vases filled with flowers picked each morning from the garden. But the hotel and many other buildings on Appledore, including Thaxter's cottage, burned to the ground in 1914. The island fell on bad times. The U.S. Navy used it for many years as a target range for cannon fire. Huge colonies of sea gulls, fairly rare there in the nineteenth century, took the place over as a rookery. Poison ivy and scrubby vegetation such as alders began to invade. Thaxter's garden lived on only in the pages of her book — and in Hassam's paintings.

But, as Lacy points out, the story of the garden has a happy ending. In 1978 Dr. John Kingsbury, director of a Cornell University marine biology

laboratory on the island, undertook to restore
Thaxter's garden, using the detailed plan in her
book. A group of volunteers now plants and
maintains the garden every summer, and once
again the glorious flowers, blooming in the sea air,
have become an attraction for tourists.

As for Thaxter's book, it too has had a renais-
sance. A few years ago a copy of the original book
was discovered in the basement archives of its
publisher, Houghton Mifflin. The book had never been opened, and the chromolithographs of
Hassam's illustrations were in better condition
than some of the originals, which had faded over
the years. With the release in 1988 of a facsimile
edition of *An Island Garden*, a new generation was
introduced to Celia Thaxter's garden.

In 1990 the Denver Museum of Art mounted
an exhibition of Childe Hassam's Isles of Shoals
paintings under the title "An Island Garden Re-
visited." The Denver Botanical Garden planned
to reproduce the original garden. The museum
exhibit opened in April at the Yale University Art
Gallery and also traveled to the National Gallery
of Art in Washington.

A hundred years after its first glory, Celia
Thaxter's and Childe Hassam's island garden
blooms again.

FRANCES TENENBAUM
Boston, 1990

AN ISLAND GARDEN DAYBOOK
BY CELIA THAXTER

WITH PAINTINGS BY
CHILDE HASSAM

January

1

2

3

4

He who is born with a silver spoon in his mouth is generally considered a fortunate person, but his good fortune is small compared to that of the happy mortal who enters this world with a passion for flowers in his soul.

January

*Ever since I could
remember anything,
flowers have been like
dear friends to me,
comforters, inspirers,
powers to uplift and to
cheer. A lonely child,
living on the lighthouse
island ten miles away
from the mainland,
every blade of grass that
sprang out of the
ground, every humblest
weed, was precious in
my sight, and I began a
little garden when not
more than five years old.*

5

6

7

8

9

10

January

11

12

13

14

It seems strange to write a book about a little garden only fifty feet long by fifteen wide! But then, as a friend pleasantly remarked to me, "it extends upward," and what it lacks in area is more than compensated by the large joy that grows out of it and its uplifting and refreshment of "the Spirit of Man."

January

15

16

17

I love to pore over every blossom that unfolds in the garden, no matter what it may be, to study it and learn it by heart as far as a poor mortal may. If one but gazes closely into a tiny flower of the pale blue Forget-me-not, what a chapter of loveliness is there!

18

19

January

The subtle knowledge of plants, instinct perhaps would be a better word, is astonishing. If you dig a hole in the ground and put into it a Rosebush, filling one side of the hole with rich earth and the other with poor soil, every root of that Rosebush will leave the poor half to inhabit the rich and nourishing portion. That is a matter of course, but the instinct of the Rose is something to think about, nevertheless.

20

21

22

23

January

24

25

26

That every plant should select only its own colors and forms from the great laboratory of Nature has always seemed to me a very wonderful thing. Each plant takes from its surroundings just those qualities which will produce its own especial characteristics and no others, never hesitating and never making a mistake.

27

28

_29_

January

_30_

_31_

*Mine is just a little old-
fashioned garden where
the flowers come
together to praise the
Lord and teach all who
look upon them to do
likewise.*

February

1

2

3

4

Much thought should be given to the garden's arrangement with regard to economy of room, where one has but a small space to devote to it.

February

When the snow is still
blowing against the
window-pane in
January and February,
and the wild winds are
howling without, what
pleasure it is to plan for
summer that is to be!
Small shallow wooden
boxes are ready, filled
with mellow earth (of
which I am always
careful to lay in a
supply before the ground
freezes in autumn),
sifted and made damp;
into it the precious seeds
are dropped with a
loving hand.

5

6

7

8

9

10

February

11

12

13

14

Often I hear people say, "How do you make your plants flourish like this?" as they admire the little flower patch I cultivate in summer, or the window gardens that bloom for me in the winter; "I can never make my plants blossom like this! What is your secret?" And I answer with one word, "Love."

February

15

_____

16

_____

17

_____

18

*It is curious that the leaf
should so love the light
and the root so hate it.*

_____

19

February

20

21

Nothing seems to me more surprising than the planting of a seed in the blank earth and the result thereof. Take a Poppy seed, for instance: it lies in your palm, the merest atom of matter, hardly visible, a speck, a pin's point in bulk, but within it is imprisoned a spirit of beauty ineffable, which will break its bonds and emerge from the dark ground and blossom in a splendor so dazzling as to baffle all powers of description.

22

23

February

24

25

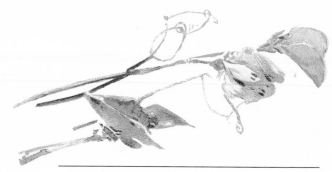

26

So deeply is the gar-
dener's instinct im-
planted in my soul, I
really love the tools with
which I work, — the
iron fork, the spade,
the hoe, the rake,
the trowel, and the
watering-pot are
pleasant objects in
my eyes.

27

28

February

29

Like the musician, the painter, the poet, and the rest, the true lover of flowers is born, not made. And he is born to happiness in this vale of tears, to a certain amount of the purest joy that earth can give her children, joy that is tranquil, innocent, uplifting, unfailing. Given a little patch of ground, with time to take care of it, with tools to work it and seeds to plant in it, he has all he needs.

March

1

2

3

The snowdrops by the
      door
Lift upward, sweet and
      pure,
Their delicate bells; and
      soon,

4

In the calm blaze of
      noon,
By lowly window-sills
Will laugh the daffodils!

   — from "March"

March

5

6

7

8

9

My upper windows all winter are filled with young Wallflowers, Stocks, single Dahlias, Hollyhocks, Poppies, and many other garden plants, which are watched and tended with the most faithful care till the time comes for transporting them over the seas to Apple-dore. A small steam tug, the Pinafore, *carries me and my household belongings over to the islands, and*

10

March

11

12

13

14

a pretty sight is the little
vessel when she starts
out from the old brown
wharves and steams
away down the beauti-
ful Piscataqua River,
with her hurricane deck
awave with green leaves
and flowers, for all the
world like a May Day
procession. My blossom-
ing house plants go also,
and there are Palms
and Ferns and many
other lovely things that
make the small boat gay
indeed.

March

15

16

17

It blossomed by the summer sea,
*   A tiny space of tangled bloom*
*   Wherein so many flowers found room,*
A miracle it seemed to be!

   — *from "My Garden"*

18

19

March

20

21

I find Sweet Peas can
hardly have too rich a
soil, provided always
that they are kept
sufficiently wet. They

22

must *have moisture,
their roots must be kept
cool and damp, — a
mulch of leaves or straw
is a very good thing to
keep the roots from

23

drying, — and they
must always be planted
as deep as possible.
Wood ashes give them a
stronger growth.*

March

As I work among my
flowers, I find myself
talking to them,
reasoning and remon-
strating with them, and
adoring them as if they
were human beings.
Much laughter I
provoke among my
friends by so doing, but
that is of no conse-
quence. We are on such
good terms, my flowers
and I!

24

25

26

27

28

29

30

31

March

The most exquisite
perfume known to my
garden is that of the
Wallflowers; there is
nothing equal to it.
They blossom early, and
generally before June
has passed they are gone,
and have left me
mourning their too
swift departure. . . .
Their thick spikes of
velvet blossoms are in
all shades of rich red,
from scarlet to the
darkest brown, from
light gold to orange;
some are purple; and
their odor, — who shall
describe it!

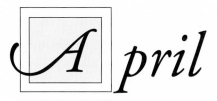

April

1

2

3

It is curious how differently certain plants feel about this matter of transplanting. The more you move a Pansy about the better it seems to like it, and many annuals grow all the better for one transplanting; but to a Poppy it means death.

4

April

The very act of planting
a seed in the earth has
in it to me something
beautiful. I always do it
with a joy that is largely
mixed with awe. I
watch my garden beds
after they are sown, and
think how one of God's
exquisite miracles is
going on beneath the
dark earth out of sight.
I never forget my
planted seeds. Often I
wake in the night and
think how the rains and
the dews have reached
to the dry shell and

5

6

7

8

9

11

12

13

softened it; how the
spirit of life begins to
stir within, and the
individuality of the
plant to assert itself;
how it is thrusting two
hands forth from the
imprisoning husk, one,
the root, to grasp the
earth, to hold itself firm
and absorb its food, the
other stretching above to
find the light, that it
may drink in the breeze
and sunshine and so
climb to its full perfec-
tion of beauty.

April

By the first of April it is time to plant Sweet Peas. From this time till the second week in May, when one may venture to transplant into the garden, the boxes containing the myriads of seedlings must be carefully watched and tended, put out of doors on piazza roofs and balcony through the days and taken in again at night, solicitously protected from too hot suns and too rough winds, too heavy rains or too low a temperature, — they require continual care.

14

15

16

17

18

April

19

20

I am always planting Shirley Poppies somewhere! One never can have enough of them, and by putting them into the ground at intervals of a week, later and later, one can secure a succession of bloom and keep them for a much longer time, — keep, indeed, their heavenly beauty to enjoy the livelong summer, — whereas, if they are all planted at once you would see them for a blissful moment, a week or ten days at most, and then they are gone.

21

22

April

23

24

25

Up from the ground, alert and bright,
*   The pansies laughed in gold and jet,*
*   Purple and pied, and mignonette*
Breathed like a spirit of delight.

Flaming the rich nasturtiums ran
*   Along the fence, and marigolds*
*   "Opened afresh their starry folds"*
In beauty as the day began . . .

*   — from "My Garden"*

26

April

27

28

29

30

If there were no other enemies which the gardener must fight, this one of weeds alone is quite enough to tax all his powers and patience.

May

1

2

3

*In the first week of May
every year punctually
arrive the barn swal-
lows and the sandpipers
at the Isles of Shoals.
This seems a very
common-place state-
ment of a very simple
fact, but would it were
possible to convey in
words the sense of
delight with which they
are welcomed on this
sea-surrounded rock!*

4

May

5

_____

6

_____

7

MAY 11. *This
morning at four o'clock
the sky was one rich red
blush in the east, over a
sea as calm as a mirror.
How could I wait for
the sun to lift its scarlet
rim above the dim sea-
line (though it rose
punctually at forty-
seven minutes past
four), when my precious
flower beds were
waiting for me! It was
not possible, and I was*

8

_____

9

_____

10

11

12

13

14

up and dressed before he
had flooded the earth
with glory. . . . All the
boxes and baskets of the
more delicate seedlings
were to be put out from
my chamber window on
flat house-top and
balcony, they and the
forest of Sweet Peas to
be thoroughly watered,
and the Pansies half
shaded with paper lest
the sun should work
them woe.

May

15

16

17

18

19

With the first faint green lines that are visible along the flower beds come the weeds, yea, and even before them; a wild, vigorous, straggling army, full of health, of strength, and a most marvelous power of growth. These must be dealt with at once and without mercy; they must be pulled up root and branch, without a moment's delay.

20

May

21

MAY 20*th. All the past days have been filled with transplanting and the most vigorous weeding. In these five days the Sweet Peas have grown so tall I was obliged to go after sticks for them to-day, wheeling my light wheelbarrow up over the hill and across the island toward the south, where among the old ruined walls of cellars and houses, and little, almost erased garden plots, the thick growth of Bayberry and Elder offered me all the sticks I needed.*

22

23

May

24

___

25

___

26

___

27

___

28

Pulling up and throw-
ing away . . . super-
fluous plants is a very
difficult thing for me
to do, . . . but it must
be done. It is a matter
of the very greatest
importance. The
welfare of the garden
depends on it. I comfort
myself as best I may by
saving all that will bear
transplanting, and then
giving them away to the
flower plots of my
fellow-gardeners on
neighboring islands.

29

May

30

31

And now, at dawn, upon the beach again,
  Kneeling I wait the coming of the sun,
Watching the looser-folded buds, and fain
  To see the marvel of their day begun.
  . . .

Red lips of roses, waiting to be kissed
  By early sunshine, soon in smiles will break.
But oh, ye morning-glories, that keep tryst
  With the first ray of daybreak, ye awake!

  — *from "Before Sunrise"*

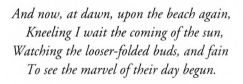

June

1

2

3

Now come the potent heats that preface summer, and everything grows and expands so fast, the process of thinning the crowded plants must begin forthwith. Oh, for days twice as long! Yet these approach the longest days of the year.

4

June

5

_____

6

_____

_____

*At bird-peep, as the
country folk have a
charming way of calling
the break of day, I am
in my dear garden, —
planting and trans-
planting, hoeing,
raking, weeding,
watering, tying up and
training those plants
that need it, and always
fighting for their
precious lives against*

7

_____

_____

8

June

9

10

11

12

*their legions of enemies.
There is a time of great
danger upon the island
from the birds when
they are migrating
northward. They come
suddenly down from the
sky in myriads, on their
way to the continent,
and I have known them
to strip the little plot of
every green shoot in a
single day, utterly bare.*

June

13

14

I do not lose patience
with the birds, however
sorely they try me. I love
them too well. How
should they know that
the garden was not
planted for them? Those
belonging to the thrush
tribe are the most
mischievous; the others
do not disturb the
flower beds so much.
The friendly robin,
though a thrush, only
comes for worms, to
which he is more than
welcome.

15

16

17

18

June

19

20

21

22

*Once a ferruginous
thrush came and stayed
a week with us in early
June. Every day when
he perched on a ridge-
pole or chimney-top and
sang, the whole family
turned out in a body to
listen, making a
business of it, attending
to nothing else while
that thrilling melody
was poured out on the
silent air. That was a
gift of the gods which
we could, none of us,
afford to neglect!*

June

It is wonderful how much work one can find to do in so tiny a plot of ground. But in the latter weeks of June there comes a time when I can begin to take breath and rest a little from these difficult yet pleasant labors; an interval when I may take time to consider, a morning when I may seek the hammock in the shady piazza, and, looking across my happy flower beds, let the sweet day sink deep into my heart.

23

24

25

26

27

28

June

29

30

As the days go on toward July, the earth becomes dry and all the flowers begin to thirst for moisture. Then from the hillside, some warm, still evening, the sweet rain-song of the robin echoes clear, and next day we wake to a dim morning; soft flecks of cloud bar the sun's way, fleecy vapors steal across the sky, the southwest wind blows lightly, rippling the water into little waves that murmur melodiously as they kiss the shore.

July

_1_

_2_

_3_

_4_

_The great mistake
which the inexperienced
gardener makes is in
leaving a morsel of the
root of a weed in the
ground. Only by
combing the earth
through and through
between the rows of
plants with the small
hand-fork (after all the
intruders have been
removed as carefully as
possible with the hand),
can you be sure that
they are gone._

July

5

6

7

8

9

Weeding all day in the hot sun; hard work, but pleasant. I find it the best way to lay two boards down near the plot I have to weed, and on them spread a water-proof, or piece of carpet, and kneeling or half reclining on this, get my face as close to my work as possible. Sitting flat on these boards, I weed all within my reach, then roll up a bit of carpet

10

July

11

12

not bigger than a
flat-iron holder, put
it at the edge of the
space I have cleared,
and lean my elbow on
it; that gives me another
arm's-length that I can
reach over, and so I go
on till all is done. I
move the rest for my
elbow here and there
as needed among the
flowers. It takes me
longer to weed than
most people, because I
will do it so thoroughly.

13

14

July

15

16

17

It is plain to see, as one gazes over the Poppy beds on some sweet evening at sunset, what buds will bloom in the joy of next morning's first sunbeams, for these will be lifting themselves heavenward, slowly and silently, but surely. To stand by the beds at sunrise and see the flowers awake is a heavenly delight. As the first long, low rays of the sun strike the buds, you know they feel the signal! A light air stirs

18

July

19

20

among them; you lift
your eyes, perhaps to
look at a rosy cloud or
follow the flight of a
caroling bird, and when
you look back again, lo!
the calyx has fallen from
the largest bud and lies
on the ground, two half
transparent, light green
shells, leaving the flower
petals wrinkled in a
thousand folds, just
released from their close
pressure. A moment
more and they are
unclosing before your
eyes.

21

22

July

23

24

25

26

27

*I am obliged to spend
a good deal of time
just now hunting and
destroying different bugs
and worms and so forth.
The blue-green aphis
appears on certain
precious Honeysuckle
buds, and must be
vigorously syringed
with fir-tree oil before
he gets a foothold and
spreads his hideous
legions everywhere.*

28

July

29

30

31

*The garden suffers from
the long drought in this
last week of July, though
I water it faithfully.
The sun burns so hot
that the earth dries
again in an hour, after
the most thorough
drenching I can give it.
The patient flowers
seem to be standing in
hot ashes, with the air
full of fire above them.
The cool breeze from
the sea flutters their
drooping petals, but
does not refresh them in
the blazing noon.*

 *August*

1

2

3

4

*Now come the most
perfect days of the year,
blue days, hot on the
continent, but heavenly
here, where the cool
breeze breathes round
the islands from the
great expanse of
whispering water.
Delightful it is to lie
here and rest and
realize all this beauty
and rejoice in all its joy!*

August

5

6

7

8

A curious plague, if I may call it so, has come upon the little garden, in the shape of the delicious edible mushrooms, Coprinus comatus, *which come up all over the place and with slow strength heave the ground and my flowers into heaps, thrusting handsome long ivory-*

9

August

10

11

12

white, umbrella-shaped
heads on stems a foot
long, up high above
and over most things
in the beds. But these
are eaten as soon as
they appear, and are
not such a very great
trial, though I would
rather they left my
dear flowers undis-
turbed.

13

August

14

15

16

When in these fresh
mornings I go into my
garden before any one is
awake, I go for the time
being into perfect
happiness. In this hour
divinely fresh and still,
the fair face of every
flower salutes me with a
silent joy that fills me
with infinite content;
each gives me its color,
its grace, its perfume,
and enriches me with
the consummation of its
beauty.

17

18

19

August

20

21

Welcome, a thousand times welcome, ye dear and delicate neighbors —
  Bird and bee and butterfly, and humming-bird fairy fine!
Proud am I to offer you a field for your graceful labors;
  All the honey and all the seeds are yours in this garden of mine.

  — from "Guests"

August

22

23

24

25

26

Now is the garden at high tide of beauty. Sweet Peas are brilliant in all their vivid tints; they are doing bravely, spite of the drought, because their roots are so well shaded. They bloom so plenteously that they can hardly be gathered, though they are cut daily. The Rose

27

August

28

29

30

31

Campion bed is a lake of delicate colors with its border of scarlet Flax. Poppies of every tint are blazing; the Hollyhocks are splendid, with their comrades the Sunflowers; every day the single Dahlias surprise me with new and unexpected flowers.

September

1

2

3

4

*The clumps of wild
Roses glow with their
red haws in the full
light; the Elder bushes
are laden with clusters
of purple berries;
Goldenrod and wild
Asters bloom, and a
touch of fire begins to
light up the Huckle-
berry bushes, "Autumn
laying here and there a
fiery finger on the
leaves."*

September

5

Already the cricket is busy
   With hints of soberer days,
And the goldenrod lights slowly
   Its torch for the autumn blaze.

O brief, bright smile of summer!
   O days divine and dear!
The voices of winter's sorrow
   Already we can hear.

   — from "Already"

6

7

8 *September*

9

10

11

Quaint little wilderness of flowers, straggling hither and thither —
  Morning-glories tangled about the larkspur gone to seed,
Scarlet runners that burst all bounds, and wander, heaven knows whither,
  And lilac spikes of bergamot, as thick as any weed.

      — *from "Guests"*

September

Climbing plants show
often a surprising degree
of intelligence, reaching
out for support as if they
had eyes to see. I have
known a vine whose
head was aimlessly
waving in the wind,
with nothing near it to
which it might cling,
turn deliberately round
in an opposite direction
to that in which it had
been growing and seize
a line I had stretched
for it to grasp, without
any help outside itself,
and within the space of
an hour's time.

12

13

14

15

16

17   *September*

18

The low-growing
Drummond's Phlox is
one of the most satis-
factory flowers for a
beginner in the art of
gardening. There is no
such word as fail in its
bright lexicon; and it
blossoms continually
from the last of June till
frost. Looking carefully
every day, by the last
half of June I find the
pale clustered flower
buds showing; then it is
not long to wait before
the whole bed is a blaze
of varied color, a deli-
cate woven carpet of
myriad vivid hues.

19

20

21

September

22

23

24

SEPTEMBER 23d.
*Now are the crickets
loud in the grass and
the Hawkweed waves in
pale yellow all over the
island, the autumn
Dandelion, starry on its
long and slender stem.
But still the garden
glows, and still autumn*

    *"Sets budding more
And still more later flowers
for the bees . . ."*

25

26

28

29

30

Sunflower tall and hollyhock, that wave in the wind together,
  Cornflower, poppy, and marigold, blossoming fair and fine,
Delicate sweet-peas, glowing bright in the quiet autumn weather,
  While over the fence, on fire with bloom, climbs the nasturtium vine!

  — from "Guests"

O ctober

1

2

3

4

If possible, it is much
the best way to begin in
the autumn to work for
the garden of the next
spring, and the first
necessity is the prepara-
tion of the soil.

October

5

6

7

8

9

*There is something
pathetic as well as
wonderful in the way
in which these growing
things of almost all
kinds meet disaster
and discouragement.
Should they suffer mis-
fortune like this, — the
lopping of a limb, or the
losing of buds, or any
sapping of their vital-
ity, — if the cause is*

_10_

_11_

_12_

October

_13_

_14_

removed, they will
try so hard to repair
damages, send out new
shoots, make strenuous
efforts to recover the
lost ground, and still
perfect blossom and
fruit as nature meant
they should. There is a
lesson to be learned of
them on which I have
often pondered.

October

15

16

17

18

The Norwegians have a
pretty and significant
word, "Opelske," which
they use in speaking of
the care of flowers. It
means literally "loving
up," or cherishing them
into health and vigor.

19

20 *October*

21

22

23

Round and round the garden rushed a sudden blast,
    Crying, "Autumn! Autumn!" shuddering as it passed.
Dry poppy-head and larkspur-spike shrill whistled in the wind,
    Together whispering, "Autumn! and Winter is behind!"

    — from "Autumn"

October

24

_____

25

_____

26

_____

The last chill asters their petals fold
  And gone is the morning-glory's bell,
But close in a loving hand I hold
  Long sprays of the scarlet pimpernel,

And thick at my feet are blossom and leaf,
  Blossoms rich red as the robes of kings;
Hardly they're touched by the autumn's grief;
  Do they surmise what the winter brings?

  — from "Flowers in October"

27

October

28

29

30

31

The withering vines are alive with many little creepers and warblers and flycatch-ers; indeed, the island is full of distinguished bird-strangers on their way south.

ovember

1

2

*When putting the
garden in order in the
autumn, all the dry
Sweet Pea vines, and
dead stalks of all kinds,
which are pulled up
to clear the ground, I
heap for shelter over
the perennials, being
careful to lay small
bayberry branches over
first, so that I may in
no way interfere with a
free circulation of air
about them.*

3

4

November

5

6

7

NOVEMBER

There is no wind at all to-night
 To dash the drops against the pane;
No sound abroad, nor any light,
 And sadly falls the autumn rain;

There is no color in the world,
 No lovely tint on hill or plain;
The summer's golden sails are furled,
 And sadly falls the autumn rain.

8   *November*

9

10

The earth lies tacitly beneath,
    As it were dead to joy or pain:
It does not move, it does not breathe, —
    And sadly falls the autumn rain.

And all my heart is patient too,
    I wait till it shall wake again;
The songs of spring shall sound anew,
    Though sadly falls the autumn rain.

November

11

12

13

*All seeds are most
interesting, whether
winged like the Dande-
lion and Thistle, to fly
on every breeze afar; or
barbed to catch in the
wool of cattle or the
garments of men, to be
borne away and spread
in all directions over the
land; or feathered like
the little polished silvery
shuttlecocks of the
Cornflower, to whirl in*

14

15

_____ 16 $\mathcal{N}ovember$
=========================

_____ 17

_____ 18

_____ 19   the wind abroad and
                                settle presently, point
                                downward, into the
                                hospitable ground; or
                                oared like the Maple,
                                to row out upon the
                                viewless tides of the air.
                                But if I were to pause
_____ 20   on the threshold of the
                                year to consider the
                                miracles of seeds alone,
                                I should never, I fear,
                                reach my garden plot
_____   at all!

November

21

22

23

24

*The dear flowers!
Summer after summer
they return to me, al-
ways young and fresh
and beautiful; but so
many of the friends who
have watched them and
loved them with me are
gone, and they return
no more.*

25

26   # November

27

28

29

30   *"Consider the Lilies,"
said the Master. Truly,
there is no more prayer-
ful business than this
"consideration" of all
the flowers that grow.*

ecember

1

2

3

*And so the ripe year
wanes. From turfy slopes
afar the breeze brings
delicious, pungent, spicy
odors from the wild
Everlasting flowers,
and the mushrooms
are pearly in the grass.
I gather the seed-pods
in the garden beds,
sharing their bounty
with the birds I love so
well, for there are
enough and to spare
for us all.*

4

December

5

6

7

Soon will set in the fitful weather, with fierce gales and sullen skies and frosty air, and it will be time to tuck up safely my Roses and Lilies and the rest for their long winter sleep beneath the snow, where I never forget them, but ever dream of their wakening in happy summers yet to be.

8

9

December

The bitter wind blows keen and drear,
  Stinging with winter's flouts and scorns,
And where the roses breathed I hear
  The rattling of the thorns.

  — *from "Mutation"*

11

12

13

December

14

15

16

17

Where are they all who wide have ranged?
Where are the flowers of other years?
What ear the wistful question hears?
Ah, some are dead and all are changed.

— *from "My Garden"*

18

December

19

20

21

Close folded, safe within the sheltering seed,
  Blossom and bell and leafy beauty hide;
Nor icy blast, nor bitter spray they heed,
  But patiently their wondrous change abide.

— *from "Rock Weeds"*

December

22

23

24

25

Year after year the island garden has grown in beauty and charm, so that in response to the many entreaties of strangers as well as friends who have said to me, summer after summer, "Tell us how you do it! Write a book about it

26

27 # December

28

29

30 and tell us how it is
done, that we may go
also and do likewise,"
I have written this
book at last. Truly it
contains the fruit of
much sweet and bitter
experience. Of what I
speak I know, and of
what I know I have
freely given.

31

AN ISLAND GARDEN DAYBOOK

was set in Adobe Garamond, a desktop computer typeface
that was designed by Robert Slimbach directly from original
type cut by the sixteenth-century French typefounders Claude
Garamond and Robert Granjon. The Adobe Expert Collec-
tion fonts give designers access to classic elements such as true
small caps, old-style figures, ligatures, and unusual fleurons.

The book was composed with Aldus PageMaker 3.01 using a
Macintosh IIx. It was prepped by Colotone Graphics, Bran-
ford, Connecticut, and printed by Ringier America, New
Berlin, Wisconsin, on Stora Matte Cream, an acid-free sheet
from Newton Falls Paper, Newton Falls,
New York.

Book design by Anne Chalmers

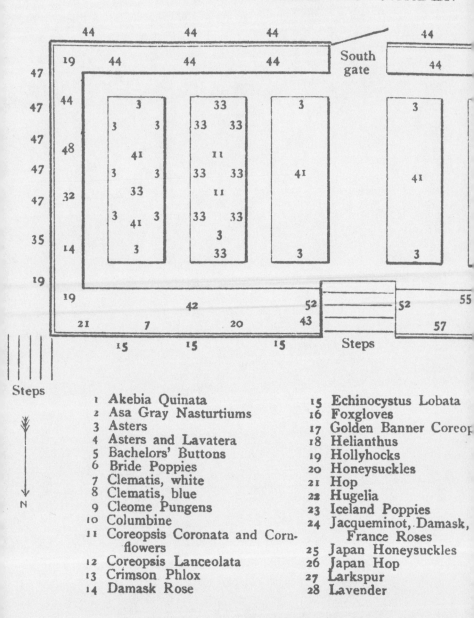

South gate

Steps

Steps

N

1 Akebia Quinata
2 Asa Gray Nasturtiums
3 Asters
4 Asters and Lavatera
5 Bachelors' Buttons
6 Bride Poppies
7 Clematis, white
8 Clematis, blue
9 Cleome Pungens
10 Columbine
11 Coreopsis Coronata and Corn-flowers
12 Coreopsis Lanceolata
13 Crimson Phlox
14 Damask Rose

15 Echinocystus Lobata
16 Foxgloves
17 Golden Banner Coreop
18 Helianthus
19 Hollyhocks
20 Honeysuckles
21 Hop
22 Hugelia
23 Iceland Poppies
24 Jacqueminot, Damask, France Roses
25 Japan Honeysuckles
26 Japan Hop
27 Larkspur
28 Lavender

NOTE. — The garden is 50 ft. long by 15 ft. wide, and i at the southwest corner slopes from the garden fence.